Where every story is a pot of gold!

Stories are the best treasure of all!
In this issue, dig up a jungle disco,
giants, Norse gods, a leprechaun, a
beast and loads of awesome animals!

This issue belongs to:

_____

Storytime™ magazine is published
every month by **Luma Works**,
Studio 2B18, Southbank Technopark,
90 London Road, London, SE1 6LN.

© Luma Creative Ltd, 2017. All rights
reserved. No part of this magazine
may be used or reproduced without
prior written permission of the
publisher. **Storytime** is a trademark
of Luma Creative Ltd. Printed by Grange.

ILLUSTRATORS:

Silvia Sponza ◉ Daffodils
Lee Cosgrove ◉ Crocodile's Silver Suit
Tim Paul ◉ Thor's Duel
Berta Sastre ◉ The Foolish Otters
Letizia Rizzo ◉ Beauty and the Beast
Pham Quang Phuc ◉ The Terrible Tiger
Daby Ihsan ◉ Jack and the Leprechaun
Tim Budgen ◉ Alphabet Zoo

www.storytimemagazine.com

Read happily ever after...

SPRING SAVINGS!

GET 50% OFF YOUR FIRST 4 ISSUES*

Daffodils

By William Wordsworth

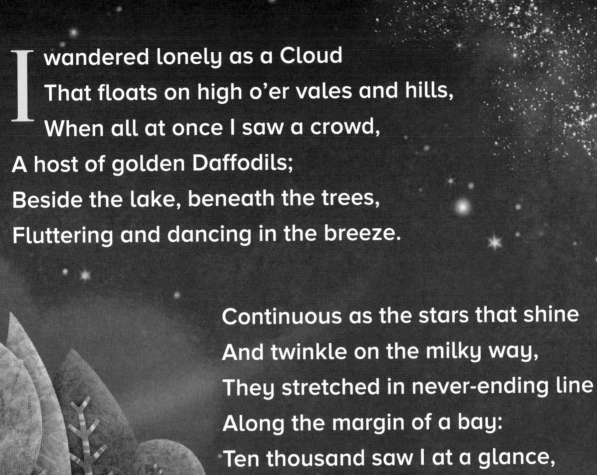

I wandered lonely as a Cloud
That floats on high o'er vales and hills,
When all at once I saw a crowd,
A host of golden Daffodils;
Beside the lake, beneath the trees,
Fluttering and dancing in the breeze.

Continuous as the stars that shine
And twinkle on the milky way,
They stretched in never-ending line
Along the margin of a bay:
Ten thousand saw I at a glance,
Tossing their heads in sprightly dance.

Crocodile's Silver Suit

By Lowri Kirkham

Little Green Crocodile was getting ready for the annual jungle roller disco. He had polished his scales, painted his claws and washed his favourite silver suit, which was drying on the line.

"I might just have a little snooze to give me some energy for later," he decided and, with a big yawn, he fell asleep under a tree in the warm summer sun.

Some time later, a funny, fluttery noise woke Little Green Crocodile and after a good stretch he went to see if his precious silver suit was dry. But it was gone!

"Where could it have gone to?" exclaimed Little Green Crocodile. "It doesn't normally wander off on its own," he thought. So he went next door to see if Zebra had seen it.

Zebra was busy setting up the music, ready for the disco.

"Zebra, have you seen my special silver suit? It seems to have wandered off," said Little Green Crocodile.

Zebra took off his headphones. "Wandered off? No, I haven't seen it, sorry. But if you need something to wear, I have this blue hat."

Little Green Crocodile tried on the blue hat, which had a large, glittery feather on the side, but it didn't fit him.

"Thank you, Zebra, but I really want my favourite silver suit."

"Maybe Rhinoceros has seen it," suggested Zebra, as he bopped along to the music.

So off went Little Green Crocodile to visit Rhinoceros, who was untangling strings of fairy lights to decorate the roller disco.

"Rhinoceros, have you seen my super-special silver suit? It's gone missing!"

"How odd," exclaimed Rhinoceros. "No sorry, I haven't seen it, but if you need something to wear I have a spare spangly purple belt."

The belt was very spangly, but it didn't fit Little Green Crocodile.

"Thank you, Rhinoceros, but I desperately want my amazing silver suit," he said.

"Maybe Porcupine has seen it," said Rhinoceros.

So off trotted Little Green Crocodile to find Porcupine, who was practising his break-dancing moves.

"Excuse me, Porcupine," said Little Green Crocodile, as Porcupine spun upside down on his head. "You haven't seen my most precious silver suit, have you? It's swanned off!"

"Hmm... how strange! No, I haven't seen it, sorry, but if you want something to wear, I have these sequinned roller boots going spare."

The yellow sequinned roller boots were indeed dazzling, but they didn't fit Little Green Crocodile's feet.

"Thank you, Porcupine, but I much prefer my tremendous silver suit!"

Little Green Crocodile left Porcupine and frantically searched the jungle for his special suit. "Where could it be? If it doesn't wander back soon, I won't be able to go to the disco," he moped.

Then, from somewhere above his head, Little Green Crocodile suddenly heard a familiar fluttery noise. He shouted, "Excuse me, fluttery thing. You haven't seen a wonderful silver suit, have you?"

A feathery face peered through the branches.

"Silver suit?" the fluttery thing squawked. Then, after a moment, a black and white bird flew down from the tree, holding something shiny under her wing.

"My suit!" cried Little Green Crocodile.

"Oh, I am sorry. I didn't realise it was your suit. I saw it hanging there and I just couldn't resist. I'm a magpie, you see, and magpies just love shiny things."

"Oh, I'm so happy to have it back," cried Little Green Crocodile. "I can go to the roller disco after all!" ➤

"Roller disco!" said the magpie. "Oh, I'd love to go to a roller disco, but I don't have a thing to wear."

Little Green Crocodile didn't like seeing his new friend looking sad, so he thought and he thought and he thought a bit more (crocodiles aren't quick thinkers) and he finally came up with a plan.

At last, it was time for the jungle roller disco! Everyone was there, including Magpie, who was wearing Zebra's glittering feathery hat, Rhinoceros's spangly belt and Porcupine's sequinned roller boots, which all fitted perfectly.

Everyone had a fantastic time, especially Little Green Crocodile – not only because he had found his favourite silver suit, but also because he had made a wonderful and *very stylish* new friend! 🌀

Thor's Duel

The giants of Jotunheim and the Norse gods of Asgard had always been enemies. The gods tried to live peacefully, but the giants were always bragging and stirring up trouble.

The chief of the gods, Odin, grew so tired of the giants' boasting that he decided to travel to Jotunheim and challenge the biggest troublemaker of them all — Hrungnir the giant — to a horse race.

"My horse can race on land, across water and through the air. It is the fastest in the nine worlds," claimed Odin.

Hrungnir, whose heart and skull were made of stone, felt no fear, but he was deeply insulted. ➳

"How dare you!" Hrungnir grunted. "My horse Gullfaxi is the fastest by far." He summoned his giant golden-maned stallion from the stables. "One of Gullfaxi's steps is equal to a hundred from your feeble creature!"

So it was agreed that Odin and Hrungnir would race. If Odin lost, he would lose his head. If Hrungnir was defeated, he promised that the giants would never again bother the gods. Odin summoned his trusty grey horse, Sleipnir, and Hrungnir was shocked to see that it had eight long, powerful legs!

The god and the giant mounted their amazing steeds, and the race began. The two rivals galloped across fields and valleys, sprinted through dense woodlands, leapt over rivers and raced over rocky mountains — and, all the time, Odin stayed in the lead, all thanks to his wonderful eight-legged horse.

Hrungnir was enraged and pushed his horse as hard as he could. He was so focused on catching up with Odin, he didn't notice that he had left his own land, and had passed through the gates of Asgard — home of the gods!

When Odin reached the hall of Valhalla, he dismounted, praising Sleipnir for a brilliant race. Hrungnir's face was purple with rage and his eyes blazed with anger.

"Come, now," said Odin. "Have a drink with the gods and let's put our differences aside. It will be good to let your horse rest." Gullfaxi did indeed look exhausted.

Hrungnir reluctantly agreed and followed Odin into the magnificent hall. Most of the gods and goddesses were there, and they were as charming as they could be to win the friendship of the menacing giant. They entertained him with stories and music, they offered him delicious food, and they made sure his cup was always full. But, deep down, the giant was still seething about losing the race and, as the night wore on, he became more and more resentful.

"More mead!" he shouted. "More bread!" He banged his fists on the table and started to insult the gods. Odin reminded him of his promise – that if the giant lost the race, he would no longer cause trouble – but when Hrungnir had drunk every last drop of mead, he threatened to kill them all! ➢

IMAGINE IT!

Odin's mythical eight-legged horse, Sleipnir, is the fastest horse in the world. What body parts could you add to an animal to make it better? Describe your imaginary animal.

"Except for Freya and Sif!" grunted Hrungnir. "They will come with me to Jotunheim and be my wives!"

Just as he said this, Sif's husband, Thor, entered Valhalla. He was furious!

"Prepare to suffer, giant!" thundered Thor. He lifted his mighty hammer, Mjölnir, ready to attack Hrungnir, but the giant sneered at him.

"Only a coward would pick a fight with someone who has no weapon." Hrungnir was unarmed. "Meet me in Jotunheim at dawn, and we will settle this argument once and for all!"

Always keen to show off his great strength, Thor agreed.

The next morning, Thor set off for the land of giants, carrying his trusty hammer. When he arrived, Hrungnir's allies seemed nervous. Hrungnir was the strongest of all the giants, so if Thor beat him, they knew they were in trouble!

However, Hrungnir's heart and skull of stone made him fearless and arrogant. He came thudding down the mountain with a massive stone shield for his defence and gripping a stone club.

"Ready?" asked Thor.

"Ready, puny fool!" grunted the giant.

Then, all of a sudden, there was a flash of lightning and a deafening rumble of thunder, created by Thor. Hrungnir dropped his shield in surprise, and Thor hurled his hammer directly at the giant.

Hrungnir quickly launched his stone club, but it was a moment too late.

In Norse mythology, the shattered pieces of Hrungnir's club landed on Midgard (the Norse name for Earth) and scattered everywhere, creating all the stones and pebbles in our soil.

The hammer and the club smashed into each other in mid-air. Thor's throw was so forceful, it shattered the club into a thousand pieces, before hitting Hrungnir's head with such speed and power, that the giant was flung across the field and into the side of the mountain he had walked down so confidently. Hrungnir was no more. The remaining giants ran into the hills, fearing for their lives.

That day, Thor left Jotunheim with two prizes – the golden-maned horse, Gullfaxi, and a tiny shard of Hrungnir's club, which had lodged itself in Thor's skull, and would stay there forever more! 🌀

The Foolish Otters

It was almost dinnertime for Mr and Mrs Jackal, and Mrs Jackal announced that she had a craving for fish.

"Melt-in-the-mouth, fresh and tasty," she sighed. "It's such a shame we don't like going in the water."

"Don't you worry," said Mr Jackal, who was craftier than a fox and wilier than a wolf. "I'll get us some fish. You just wait and see." And he slinked away through the bushes, hoping to steal a fisherman's catch.

When Mr Jackal reached the river, he saw two sleek otters on the bank, staring intently at the water as it flowed by.

"There!" cried one, pointing out a giant fish with its paw. "It's huge!"

In a flash, the otter dived into the water and caught the fish by the tail. But the fish was big and slippery, and it soon wriggled away.

"Quick! It's escaping," yelped the otter to its friend. "Help me!"

The second otter plunged into the river. Between the two of them, they caught the massive fish and dragged it onto the riverbank.

"Let's divide it in two," said the second otter, excited by their clever catch. "I'll take the head!" he said.

"I don't think so!" said the first otter. "The head is mine – that's where all the best meat is. I jumped in first. You can have the tail."

"Forget it!" said the second otter. "The fish would have got away if it wasn't for me! You get the tail, I get the head."

The otters carried on like this for some time, each one arguing bitterly that it deserved the biggest bit. Meanwhile, Mr Jackal's mouth watered at the sight of the fat, juicy fish that lay before them.

Learn About It!

Can you find out five facts about otters? Make your own mini animal factfile!

When it seemed like the otters would never reach a decision, Mr Jackal stepped forward and said politely, "Friends, I saw what happened just now. Perhaps I can help you to settle your argument?"

Of course, all otters know that jackals are famous for their clever minds, so they willingly accepted his offer.

Very quickly, Mr Jackal bit into the fish, dividing it into three sections — a head, a tail, and the big fat middle — the best bit.

"Here, you can have the head because you were the quickest to jump in the river," said Mr Jackal, pushing it towards the first otter. "And you can have the tail for helping out," he said, pushing the tail towards the second otter.

"And I get the middle for putting an end to your argument!" Then Mr Jackal grabbed the biggest, tastiest hunk of fish and hurried back to Mrs Jackal.

The two otters studied their measly morsels and looked at each other in dismay. The clever jackal had won the best bit of fish — and all because the otters had been so greedy and foolish! ⑥

Beauty and the Beast

Once upon a time, there was a farmer who had three daughters. The youngest daughter was so pretty that everyone called her Beauty.

This made her older sisters jealous and they were cruel to her, but Beauty was too kind-hearted to notice. "Perhaps they're having a bad day," she thought.

One day, the farmer had to go away to sell his produce. The two older sisters nagged their father to return with gowns and jewels, but Beauty stayed silent.

"What would you like, Beauty?" asked the farmer.

"If it's no trouble, Father, I would like a rose, as we don't have any growing in our garden, and I like them so much," said Beauty. »→

As it happened, the farmer's trip went badly, and he lost lots of money. He was so upset about it, he forgot his way home and got lost in the forest. It began to rain heavily, and the wind was howling wildly. The farmer was beginning to fear for his life when he saw a light through the trees. He followed it and was amazed to find a grand castle before him.

He led his horse to the stables, then knocked at a rather grand front door, but nobody answered. The door swung open, so he stepped inside, and called, "Hello!". Nobody came.

In the dining room, he found a table laden with food and set for one. He dried himself by the fire and waited for someone to appear, but nobody did. At last, he was so hungry, he helped himself to the fine food.

After his meal, the farmer set off to look for someone to thank, but every room he looked inside was empty.

Eventually, he reached a room with a wide, comfortable-looking bed. The farmer was so weary, he couldn't resist. He climbed in and dozed off.

When he woke the next morning, he was surprised to find a new suit lying at the end of his bed. He dressed and returned to the dining room, where he found breakfast waiting for him. "Thank you for your generosity," called the farmer. "I am grateful."

When he stepped outside again, he was taken aback by the beauty of the castle garden. On his way to the stables, he walked under a rose arch, which gave off a sweet and wonderful scent. Remembering Beauty's request, he plucked several red roses for her. In an instant, a great hairy beast appeared before him. It seemed to be half-man and half-bear, and it had a fearsome expression.

"This is how you repay me?" said the strange creature. "You steal from me!"

The farmer fell to his knees, thanking the beast for his kindness and offering his apologies. "I meant you no harm, my lord," he cried. "I was picking them for my daughter. She loves roses!"

"Ah, you have a daughter?" said the creature. "In that case, I will make a deal with you. You can have my roses, but either you or your daughter must return here in one week."

Quaking with fear, the farmer agreed.

"You may call me Beast," said the monster. "And, as a reward for making your promise, you will find a chest of treasure next to your horse."

Beast was true to his word. The farmer carried the chest home, thinking, "At least my daughters won't have to live in poverty when I am gone.."

When he reached home, he shed tears as he told his daughters what had happened. The two eldest sisters didn't care. They grabbed the treasures and said spitefully, ≫→

"This is all your fault, Beauty. If you hadn't asked for a stupid rose, Father wouldn't have to live with a monster."

But Beauty remained calm. "Father doesn't have to suffer at all," she said, "because I will be going in his place."

"No! I'll never let that happen," cried the farmer. In the coming week, he did all he could to persuade Beauty to stay, but she had made up her mind. She was going to Beast's castle.

When it was time for her to leave, her sisters seemed glad to be rid of her. The farmer travelled with her and, when they arrived at the castle, Beast welcomed them. Beauty gasped at the sight of his strange face, but she curtseyed politely and smiled at him.

"You are a good man for keeping your promise," said Beast to the farmer. "But now you must leave."

Beauty hugged her father tightly and tried hard to be brave. It took all her strength to hold back her tears.

She waved goodbye and, when she turned round, Beast had disappeared.

Beauty decided to put her fears aside and explore her new home. Before long, she found a door with the words 'Beauty's Chamber' engraved upon it. Inside, there was a huge four-poster bed and a library containing every book Beauty could ever wish to read.

"This should take my mind off things," she thought. Beauty loved books.

She opened one and was surprised to find these words written inside:

Welcome, Beauty, banish fear,
You are queen and mistress here.
Speak your wishes and your needs,
We are here to do your deeds.

"If only that were true," sighed Beauty. "I wish so badly to see my father."

No sooner had she said it than the mirror by her side showed her father arriving home. She had never seen him looking so sad, but she couldn't help notice her sisters' joyful faces.

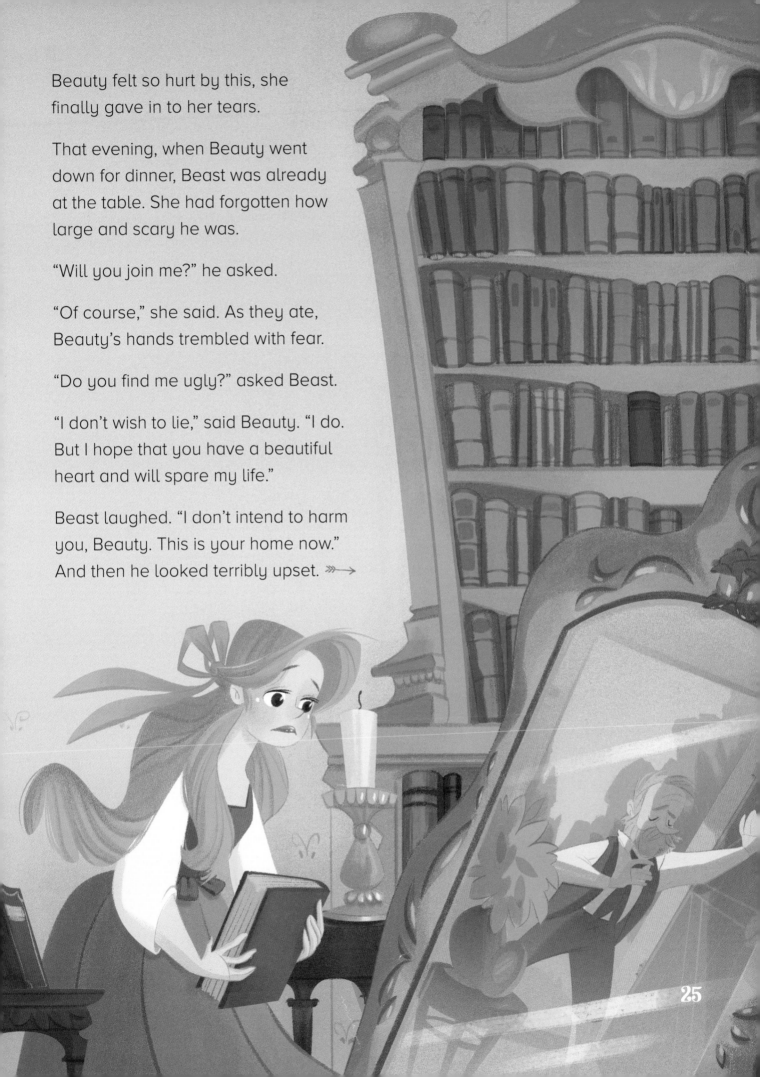

Beauty felt so hurt by this, she finally gave in to her tears.

That evening, when Beauty went down for dinner, Beast was already at the table. She had forgotten how large and scary he was.

"Will you join me?" he asked.

"Of course," she said. As they ate, Beauty's hands trembled with fear.

"Do you find me ugly?" asked Beast.

"I don't wish to lie," said Beauty. "I do. But I hope that you have a beautiful heart and will spare my life."

Beast laughed. "I don't intend to harm you, Beauty. This is your home now." And then he looked terribly upset. »→

"You are right. I am ugly,

Count It!

How many red roses can you count in this picture? Write your answer here!

but I do have a good heart."

"I am sure you do," said Beauty, suddenly feeling sorry for him.

"If you need anything at all, all you have to do is ask for it," said Beast.

They talked for the rest of the evening and, when it was time for bed, Beast asked, "Will you marry me, Beauty?"

Beauty was shocked. Fearful that she would make him angry, she looked at the floor and said, "No, Beast. I can't."

In a sorrowful voice, Beast wished her goodnight and left the room.

For three months, Beauty enjoyed all that the castle had to offer. Every evening, she looked forward to dining with Beast and they chatted for many hours.

And every night, before bed, he asked Beauty to marry him. She always said no but, the more she got to know Beast, the worse it made her feel.

"It's such a pity that someone so kind and funny and good-hearted should look so beastly," she thought.

One day, she asked the magic mirror for a glimpse of her father and was upset to see him lying in bed, looking gravely ill. That evening, she begged Beast to let her go home.

"The very thought of him suffering makes me despair," she said.

"Then you may go," sighed Beast. "I don't want you to be unhappy, but I will die of grief if I don't see you again."

"I'll go for just for one week," said Beauty. "I promise you!"

So it was agreed. Beast told Beauty that she would wake up the following morning in her father's house. He gave her a magical golden ring and told her to place it on her bedside table at the end of her week away.

That night, when Beast said goodnight, he looked greatly troubled. Beauty hated to see him so upset.

When Beauty woke up in her father's house the following morning, she forgot all about her worries.

The farmer was overjoyed to see his daughter alive and looking so radiant. Instantly, he felt much better. Beauty discovered that her two sisters had got married, and rarely visited their father. So, to make him happy, she invited her sisters for a family lunch.

Both sisters had thought that Beauty was dead so, when they saw her looking more beautiful than ever and wearing an expensive gown, they were sour-faced with jealousy.

Beauty told them about her promise to Beast, and instead of thinking, "Poor sister, living with such a beast," the jealous sisters plotted and schemed.

"Let's keep her here for more than a week," said one to the other. "Then the stupid beast will die or he might get so angry that he eats her!"

So the two sisters, who had always been so unkind to Beauty, suddenly behaved like they were her friends.

The next few days were the happiest Beauty had ever known with her family and, when it was time ≫→

for her to return, her sisters pretended to weep. They begged her to stay.

"A few more days can't hurt," they said. So Beauty stayed with them and, every time she said she had to go, the sisters pleaded with her to stay longer.

Beauty was happy that her sisters were being kind, but she missed Beast and couldn't stop thinking about him.

On her twelfth night away, she was woken by a vivid and disturbing dream. In it, she had seen Beast lying in the castle garden under the rose arch.

He looked like he was dying.

"What have I done?" she despaired. At once, Beauty placed the gold ring on her bedside table.

When she woke in the morning, she was back in Beast's castle. She leapt from her bed and ran to the gardens.

When she saw Beast lying on the ground, she cried, "Oh, Beast, please forgive me! Don't die!"

She rested her head on his chest and said, "I will marry you. I love you and

I've missed you so much. I would rather marry a beast with a good heart than a man with a beastly heart!"

Beauty heard Beast's heart suddenly beat strongly. When she looked up at him, she was amazed to see that he was no longer a monstrous creature, but a handsome man!

"Where is my Beast?" asked Beauty.

"I am him," said the man. "I am a prince who was cursed by a wicked witch who wanted revenge on my family.

The only way her spell could be lifted was if someone fell in love with me. Beauty, I thank you with all my heart."

Beauty and the prince embraced. That very day, they left the castle to return to the prince's kingdom. On the way, they stopped at her father's cottage. The farmer was overjoyed to hear his daughter's wonderful news, but the sisters – well, you can guess!

Needless to say, there was only one happy every after in this story! ⑥

The Terrible Tiger

Deep in the beautiful Korean countryside, there was a little village where everything was calm and peaceful – except for when the tiger that lived in the hills above the village was bad-tempered.

When the tiger was in a bad mood, her roar was so loud and so terrible that it shook the houses and made everyone quake with fear. When people heard the tiger roar like this, they rushed inside, locked their doors and hid away.

One day, the tiger had been roaring rather a lot, because she couldn't find any food. She was hungry and grumpy and so desperate for something to eat that she decided to creep down the hill into the little village and look for dinner. As she quietly padded down the pathways and stalked along the alleys, she was stopped in her tracks by an alarming cry.

"Waah! Waah! Waah!" it went. The tiger had never heard anything like it before. She followed the wailing until she came to a small house. Through an open window, she saw a tiny baby lying in a cot. Its little face was scrunched up and red, and its cry was ear-splittingly loud.

"How annoying," thought the tiger. "I'd better gobble it up to give us some peace."

The tiger was about to leap through the open window and catch the baby in her claws, when the infant's mother came into the room.

The tiger speedily slunk out of sight, but stayed by the window, waiting for her moment. The mother lifted the baby from the cot and tried to comfort it.

"Shhh!" said the mother, "or Mr Fox will growl at us. Mr Fox doesn't like noise."

But the baby didn't care. It carried on screaming. "Waah! Waah! Waah!"

The mother rocked her baby, but it still yowled.

"Shhh!" said the mother, "or Mrs Bear will grizzle at us. Mrs Bear doesn't like noise."

But the baby didn't care. It carried on screaming. "Waah! Waah! Waah!"

"This baby is scared of nothing!" thought the tiger. "Not even a fox or a bear can make it be quiet."

The mother fed her baby and sang a lullaby, but the baby still howled.

"Shhh!" said the mother, "or the Terrible Tiger will roar at us. The Terrible Tiger doesn't like noise."

"Ah," thought the tiger. "That will make the noisy little tyke be quiet. Let's see how scared it is of me..."

But the baby didn't care. It carried on screaming and showed no sign of fear at all. "Waah! Waah! Waah!"

The tiger was shocked. She had never met a human who wasn't scared of her.

"I can't have this!" she thought. "I'd better eat the child just to teach everyone here a lesson!"

And she was just about to pounce through the window, when the mother said, "Shhh! Look! A persimmon!"

At that, the baby stopped crying and fell completely silent.

"A persimmon?" thought the tiger. "A persimmon? What is this monster that's more fearsome than a fox, scarier than a bear and more terrifying than a tiger?"

Her heart pounding with fear, the tiger looked left and right for the persimmon, and then she bounded out of the village before the horrible beast could catch up with her. From that day on, she never crept into the village again and she didn't even roar, for fear that the petrifying persimmon would track her down! ⑥

TASTE IT!

A persimmon is a type of fruit. It looks like an orange tomato and has a texture like a plum. In Korea, they are often eaten dried, and they taste sweet and delicious – a bit like figs or dates with honey. Why not try one?

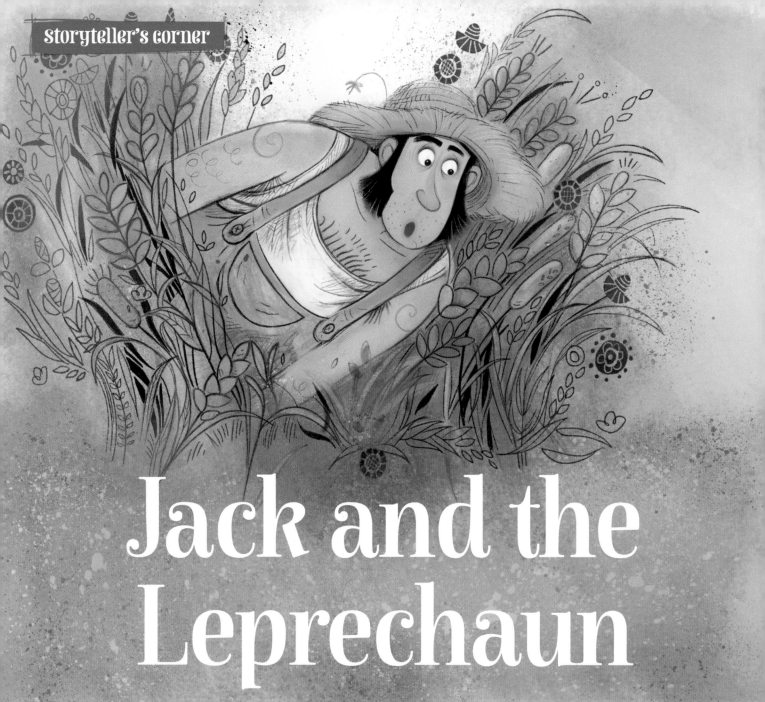

Jack and the Leprechaun

Farmer Jack was busy working in his fields one day when he heard whistling and a strange *tap-tap-tapping* sound coming from the hedgerow.

"What can it be?" wondered Jack, and he put down his scythe and went to investigate. He followed the whistle and the tapping all the way to the bushes, where he found a little man making a shoe. He was tapping at the sole with a tiny hammer. The man was no higher than Jack's knee, and he had a shock of bright red hair, a red beard, and mischief in his eyes. He wore a smart green hat and a suit, and he was whistling a merry tune. The little man was a leprechaun, of course – and Jack knew it right away.

Now Jack remembered that, according to local legend, all he had to do was keep his eyes on the leprechaun and the little man would lead him to a pot of gold at the end of the rainbow. So, Jack stepped forward and said, "Good morning, sir! Fine work you're doing!"

If the leprechaun was shocked to see a stranger, he didn't show it. "Why, thank you, sir," he said, smiling.

"What shall I call you?" asked Jack.

"You may call me the sun and the moon and in between," said the leprechaun, grinning.

"That's a big name for a little fella!" laughed Jack.

"And Jack is a little name for a big fella like you!" chuckled the leprechaun.

"How did you know my name?" asked Jack in surprise.

"I've been living on this farm for a lot longer than you have, lad," said the leprechaun. "Maybe we could drink a toast to that. I have a bottle in the bushes." And he pointed behind Jack.

But Jack wasn't fooled. He didn't take his eyes off the little leprechaun. "I'm fine, thank you," said Jack.

"Beautiful day, isn't it now?" asked the leprechaun, pointing up at the sky.

Jack agreed, but he didn't look up. He kept his eyes fixed on the wee man.

"Is that a bird dining on your crops over there?" asked the leprechaun, pointing across the field.

Jack just smiled and kept on staring. The little man tried everything he could to make Jack look away, but it was no use. Jack was determined.

At last, Jack said, "Perhaps you could show me where your pot of gold is?"

The leprechaun grumbled, but he had no choice – it was leprechaun law. If you were fool enough to be caught by a human, you had to do as they asked!

"Sure enough," sighed the leprechaun. "Follow me, but it's not at the end of the rainbow, like you think it is!"

The leprechaun set off, mumbling and moaning, with Jack at his side. All the time, Jack watched the leprechaun so he couldn't get away. His stomach flipped with excitement at the thought of gold. They walked across the field, climbed over a stile, crossed a stream and finally reached a field covered with thousands of golden dandelions.

They walked through the flowers until the leprechaun pointed at one of the dandelions. "That's the one, Jack. Dig there – that's where you'll find the pot of gold. Now, I'm behind on my cobbling, so I'd better be off."

"Do you promise?" asked Jack. "Do you swear the gold's under there?"

"By leprechaun law, I swear." The little man nodded, but he had a glint in his eye as he said it.

Jack looked down at the dandelion and, when he looked up again, the leprechaun had already gone.

Now Jack had a problem – he had nothing to dig with, so he decided to set off for home to grab his spade. Before he left, he pulled off a sock and laid it over the dandelion, so he could find it easily when he returned. Jack did think he was being clever.

When he reached home, he couldn't wait to tell his wife Mary about his good fortune.

"We're going to be rich!" he cried, and he told her about his meeting with the little leprechaun.

39

Jack fetched his spade and, with Mary by his side, dashed back to the dandelion field. But, when he got there, he could hardly believe his eyes. Every single flower had a sock like Jack's on top of it. The little leprechaun had tricked him!

Jack threw down his spade in frustration – he could be digging the field for years and still not find the pot of gold. His wife Mary burst out laughing. "Well, we'll save a lot of money on socks, anyway!"

There was nothing Jack could do but laugh along with her. 🌀

ODD SOCK OUT!

One of the socks in this picture is different from the others – can you spot it? Tick this box when you find it!

Alphabet Zoo

**Our zoo is a secret, but you've got the key.
Now let's meet animals starting with C!**

We rush through the gates to see Bonnie and Boo,
And they take us to view a white **Cockatoo**.
For fifty years, it's been screeching and squawking.
Mimicking people laughing and talking!

It bobs up and down and shows off its crest,
Then calls, "Hello, gorgeous, you are the best!"
We could stay all day with this brilliant bird,
But it's time to meet someone funny and furred ...

Hello, gorgeous!

41

The **Coati** – a cutie, with a long wriggly nose,
A straight stripy tail, and strong claws and toes.
The Coati's an acrobat up in the trees,
And walks upside down with the greatest of ease!

It's from South America, like its good neighbour,
The cool **Capybara** – the web-footed wader.
It's hairy and pig-like but, boy, can it swim,
And no other rodent is bigger than him!

Next, the **Chameleon** – the colourful lizard,
It changes its hues like a reptile wizard!
From yellow to green and orange to blue,
That's how it tells you it's in a good mood!

The **Camel** next door isn't quite so polite.
When it has the hump, it can spit and can bite!
This one's a dromedary, with one lump, not two,
Where it stores lots of fat for times short of food.

It bats its long lashes, then gives a short blow.
Camel for saying "Let's make friends", you know!

ANIMAL FACT!

Chameleons are the only animal to have eyes that look in two different directions at the same time. They can even zoom in on objects they're looking at, like a camera! Download our Alphabet Zoo Factsheet from storytimemagazine.com/free

storytime playbox

Solve our fairy-tale teasers, be an animal artist, make a bright and colourful daffodil decoration, and win a pot of gold!

1 BEAST'S SECRET MESSAGE

Help Beauty solve this picture puzzle and discover a hidden message from Beast in the coloured squares.

1. M I R R O R
2. C A S T E L
3. F A R M E R
4. R A I N
5. P L A T E
6. R O S E
7. F I R E
8. R I N G
9. C H E S T
10. H O R S E

② COOL CAMEL

Use this grid as your guide to draw the other half of the camel's face, then colour it in!

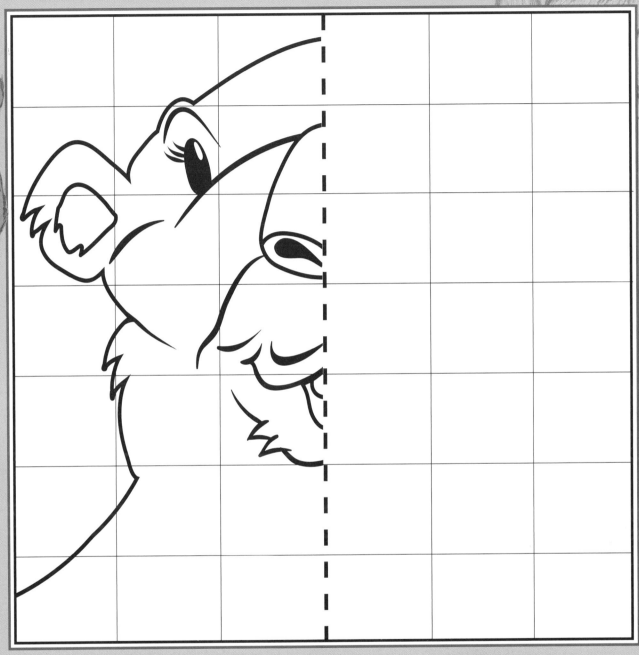

③ GO FISHING

The otters have lost the head and tail of their fishy dinner. See if you can spot them in our Playbox pages before Mr Jackal eats them. Colour in this fish when you've found them!

④ WHO IS IT?

Three animals are hiding behind our jungle disco mirror ball. Can you work out who they are? Write their names below.

1. _ _ _ _ _ _ _ _

2. _ _ _ _ _ _ _ _ _ _ _

3. _ _ _ _ _ _ _ _ _ _ _ _

WHO'S MISSING?

Follow the clues to work out which animal from **Crocodile's Silver Suit** is missing from behind the mirror ball.

1. I have a blue hat.

2. I love to DJ!

3. I'm black and white.

⑤ HOW MANY LEGS?

Count how many legs the characters in our Norse myth, **Thor's Duel**, have. Write the numbers below each character, then do the sums!

46

⑥ MAKE A DAFFODIL WREATH!

Ask a grown-up!

Brighten up your bedroom door with a colourful wreath of paper daffodils. It's fun and easy to make!

- Place a large dinner plate on a big sheet of thick green card and draw around it with a pencil.
- Place a smaller plate in the centre of the circle and draw around that too. You need to make a ring wide enough to stick paper flowers to.
- Use a craft knife or scissors to cut out the ring.
- On bright yellow card, draw a flower with six pointed petals. (Print off our template to draw around if you like – see below.)
- Repeat as many times as you need to so that you cover the green ring. Stick on your yellow flowers.
- To make them look like daffodils, you need a centre for each flower. You can use a yellow or orange mini cupcake case for this or a painted egg carton. You can also roll up a wide strip of yellow or orange card until it's big enough.
- When you have your daffodil centres, stick the base of each one to a yellow flower.
- Use tape to stick a length of yellow, orange or green ribbon, wool or string to the back of your wreath, then hang it somewhere to brighten up your room.

TIP! **Download and print out our daffodil flower templates to draw around from storytimemagazine.com/free**

⑦ QUICK QUIZ!

Which animal did the baby's mother mention first in our Korean tale, **The Terrible Tiger?**

 **a.** Mrs Bear

 **b.** Mr Fox

 **c.** Mr Lion

ANSWERS: 1. Beast's Secret Message – I am a prince; 4. Who is it? – 1. Magpie, 2. Crocodile, 3. Rhinoceros, and Zebra is missing; 5. How Many Legs? – 10; 7. Quick Quiz – Mr Fox.

47

GOING FOR GOLD!

How to Play

You need two dice and two players for this game. Also print off our Leprechaun Game Counters from **storytimemagazine.com/free**. Before you begin, choose whether you want to be the Sun Leprechaun or the Moon Leprechaun. The aim of the game is to place a counter on every one of your coloured circles – see below!

★ Position your game counters at the **START** and choose a player to roll first.

★ Player 1 rolls two dice and adds up the numbers.

  • If you're the Sun Leprechaun, you can only place counters on the red numbered circles.
  • If you're the Moon Leprechaun, you can only place counters on the yellow numbered circles.

★ If you roll a number that belongs to you, place a counter on it. If not, better luck next time!

★ Players take it in turns to roll. The first player to cover all their coloured circles with counters wins the lucky pot of gold!

START

Follow the rainbow to the pot of gold – and improve your maths skills along the way. We wish you all the luck of the Irish!

LUCKY CLOVER
When you've got five counters on the board, roll two dice on this four-leaf clover. If you roll a lucky 7, you get an extra roll next turn!

10

6

7

11

9

8

10

12

STORY MAGIC

Adventurous, fearless and cheeky kids star in our latest book recommendations – make sure you don't miss them!

BOOKS OF THE MONTH!

Two more great books to buy or loan from your library this month. They're out now!

THE NAUGHTY, NAUGHTY BADDIES by Mark Sperring and illustrated by David Tazzyman (Bloomsbury) is a madcap, anarchic adventure featuring three rebellious kids, their cat and a wicked, wicked plan involving the Queen's favourite pooch, Little Doggy Woof-Woof. Completely silly and very funny, these are the kind of baddies you can't help rooting for.

THE SECRET OF BLACK ROCK by Joe Todd-Stanton (Flying Eye Press). Erin longs to see whether the legend of black rock – a sharp, treacherous mass that has sunk many a boat – is true. But when she finally plunges the depths of the mystery, what she discovers is far more magical and beautiful than she ever imagined. And it's up to Erin to share the secret and save the day! Fans of Joe's first book, *Arthur and the Golden Rope*, will love this too!

St Patrick's Day Stories!

Celebrate St Patrick's Day by reading books from great Irish illustrators and authors! Here are three of our favourites.

1. ONCE UPON AN ALPHABET by Oliver Jeffers. A beautiful book with 26 mini stories in one. You won't mind reading it again and again – and you will! (Harper Collins Children's Books)

2. SHH! WE HAVE A PLAN by Chris Haughton. A great companion to *The Naughty, Naughty Baddies,* as it features another goofy gang with a plan. Every page is a work of art. (Walker Books)

3. THE LONELY BEAST by Chris Judge. We've raved about *The Snow Beast* before, but recommend you go back to the first in this fab series of books, which sees a lonesome beast set out on a quest for friendship. (Andersen Press)

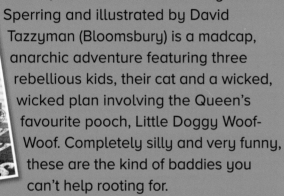

WIN!

COMPETITION!

Win beautiful copies of our featured Books of the Month – *The Naughty, Naughty Baddies* and *The Secret of Black Rock.* All you have to do to enter is answer our monthly spine question. Find out more at: **storytimemagazine.com/win**